Boxes

by Miriam Sklar

ISBN: 978-1-338-75072-0
Illustrated by John Lund

Published by Scholastic Inc., 557 Broadway, New York, NY 10012

10 9 8 7 6 5 4 68 25 26 27/0

Printed in Jiaxing, China. First printing, January 2021.

Boxes can be big.

Boxes can be small.

Boxes can be wide.

Boxes can be square.

Boxes can be round.

Boxes can be tall.

Boxes can fall!